Odyssey Family Systems Companion Guide

By Kathryn Hayward, M.D.
Illustrated By Maia Ibar

Digital conversion of illustrations,
creation of graphic of Odyssey Journey paradigm,
and cover design by Jack Temple

Published in association with
International Integrators and with Odyssey Journey:
A Collaborative Approach to Wellness.

2019 Edition

ISBN-13: 9781790346042

Dedication

With love and gratitude,
I dedicate this work to my greatest teachers,
my parents, my husband, David L. Thomas, Jr.,
our son, our daughter, their spouses and our grandchildren.

Table of Contents

Acknowledgements

WITH ALL MY HEART, I wish to thank my family system members, friends, mentors, colleagues, students and Odyssey participants.

I also want to acknowledge the encouragement and support of members of the International Integrators community and, in particular, Bill Manahan, Brooke Anderson, Kristy King, Jack Temple and Maia Ibar. International Integrators is a collaborative, global community dedicated to the promotion of Integrative Health.

Introduction

My Dream

LIKE MANY REVELATIONS, the creation of the Odyssey Family Systems Companion Guide was influenced by a dream. In July of 2013, my husband, David, was driving the two of us from Martha's Vineyard in Massachusetts to New York City. We were speaking about our current favorite subject, the International Integrators project on which we were collaborating with a number of other people interested in Integrative Health. I suddenly felt an overwhelming need to sleep, and got comfortable in the passenger's seat and slept for 45 minutes. At other times in my life, this sort of sudden need to sleep has occurred, and oftentimes an important dream has emerged. This time, the dream offered two gifts: the name *Odyssey Family Systems*, and the image of the infinity symbol being used for the Parts of Self illustrations.

The next night, we were having dinner with four medical students in New York City. Three of the students had recently experienced an Odyssey Family Systems Workshop, and the fourth was asking about it. As David and I sat listening to the students excitedly tell of their experiences with the workshop,

I was filled with a sense of awe and gratitude for the privilege of being present to this conversation. One of the students particularly recalled the Caretaker/Caregiver themes. Another was touched by the Judge/Globalizer and Performer/ Perfectionist Parts of Self. Their animated recounting of the experience stayed with me that night and through my night's sleep. The next morning, I knew that a piece of writing had to come so that these students, and others, could have something to reference as they worked with the themes that so deeply touched them.

I massaged the script of the workshop. During that process, the content spoke to me, telling me that this would be a Companion Guide and that it needed a lot of illustrations. I asked Maia Ibar to consider creating the artistic offerings of the Guide, and am deeply grateful for her extraordinary contributions. Jack Temple then joined us to convert Maia's illustrations into digital form, and my husband David converted the manuscript into an e-book. Our collaborative process has been one of the greatest joys of my life.

I see possible future versions of this Guide having multiple media enfolded within it. There are myriad opportunities for those who use it to collaborate, co-create and describe their stories that so richly emerge from using the Guide.

Backstory

For twenty years, I practiced primary care internal medicine at Massachusetts General Hospital and Harvard Medical School in Boston, Massachusetts. My experience in that world taught me that conventional medicine is wonderfully powerful for acute disease conditions and immunizations, and narrowly focused when it comes to chronic conditions, wellness and prevention. More than ninety percent of my work and that of my primary care colleagues was in the areas of chronic conditions, wellness and prevention, and, therefore, I found that my conventional medicine training needed augmentation.

My patients' experiences led me to become curious about and explore disciplines beyond the confines of the conventional medicine system, including acupuncture, herbs, jin shin jyutsu, massage, meditation, homeopathy, structural integration, osteopathy, yoga, qi gong, tai chi, the Feldenkrais method, the Egoscue method, energy medicine, family constellation work, resonance repatterning and plant-based nourishment. I have come to regard these and others as "mind/body/spirit" disciplines. My explorations opened numerous doors that enriched my own healing journey and gave me more to offer during the years within which many of my relationships were regarded as those of doctor and patient.

In 2004, I created an integrative medicine practice called *Odyssey Journey: A Collaborative Approach To Wellness* (www.odysseyjourney.com). The definition of what is currently called "integrative medicine" has evolved and will continue to do so. Eventually, I hope that we will talk animatedly about "Collaborative Health and Healing." For now, the term is "integrative medicine", and I offer this definition:

"Integrative medicine considers the whole person—body, mind, spirit and community, including all aspects of lifestyle. It emphasizes the promotion of health, the prevention of illness and the treatment of disease. Communication and collaboration form the foundation of all therapeutic relationships. Integrative medicine brings together the best in conventional medicine, whole, plant-based food, movement and mind/body/spirit disciplines."

People often come to Odyssey because they have health issues for which they have sought care in the conventional medicine system and they want a conventionally-trained doctor to help them look at their challenges more holistically. In Odyssey, they think of themselves as "participants", not "patients", who partner with me and other practitioners.

I offer for your consideration two more definitions:

I regard *health* as *emerging consciousness*
I regard *disease* as a reflection of *imbalance* that can be guided toward balance when one engages in the work of becoming conscious

Odyssey participants, team members and I collaborate to discover and explore past injuries that participants are holding, that are forming blockages or hindrances to their living the lives to which they aspire. Together, we move energy, clearing the imbalances in their systems that are contributing to their having medical and other challenges.

This *Companion Guide* is focused on one important discipline that is useful in this process: that of the Internal Family System and the External Family System, which I refer to as the Family Constellation. Family System work has been explored, robustly developed and described over the past few decades by many visionary luminaries. I humbly offer my insights to that body of work. The paradigm described in this Guide is called *Odyssey Family Systems.*

Because I love story and the power of story, I have given names to various *parts of self.* Some of these names have emerged from work I have done with Odyssey participants, and I am delighted at the spirit of collaboration that has contributed to this current manifestation.

This Companion Guide's prior publication has been enjoyed by people who have experienced the Odyssey Family Systems workshops, Odyssey individual sessions, or by those who are well versed in Family Systems work. In addition, people for whom this work is new have found the Guide to be helpful.

This is meant to be a guide to further your individual and group work, or Odyssey Chosen Family Circle work, as you experience your process of *emerging consciousness.* I am honored to be joining you for this part of your journey, and to collaborate with you in your explorations and illuminations.

Odyssey Family Systems

(FIG. 1) **I came across** these two trees during a recent walk in the woods on Mallorca.

(Fig. 2) Here is a closer look at the roots and base of one of these trees.

(Fig. 3) Here is a seed like the one that gave birth to the larger of the two trees. After the seed was planted, it sprouted roots, looking for nourishment in the earth.

(Fig. 4) Then a tendril pushed its way toward the surface of the earth, looking for sun, air and rain. The seed was becoming a seedling. The tendril and roots had to work around obstacles that they encountered in the earth that surrounded them, such as the rocks and roots of other trees.

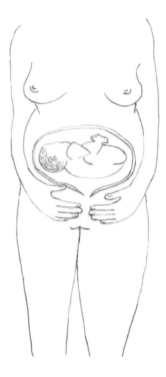

(Fig. 5) When we are in the wombs of our mothers, we are like this seed. Even as we are in the form of just a few cells, we are already connected to our mother's energy system. As we grow during our time within her, we energetically experience life as she is experiencing it.

(Fig. 6) A baby growing in the womb of a woman who is excited to be expecting, working in a job she loves, exercising every day, eating healthfully and enjoying loving relationships has one type of gestational experience.

(Fig. 7) A baby growing in the womb of a terrified woman who is living in a war zone has a very different type of gestational experience.

(Fig. 8) When a baby is born, it needs many things.
There is one thing the baby needs most, however.

(Fig. 9) How do we define Love?

CONDITIONAL LOVE

(Fig. 10) "I love you for what you do for me, what you give to me."

UNconditional LOVE

(Fig. 11)

"I see you."
"I hear you."
"I love you for where you are in your journey and how you are doing your journey."

Unconditional Love: The Connecting-Up Self

A CHILD IN a home within which Unconditional Love is present is cocooned by family and friends.

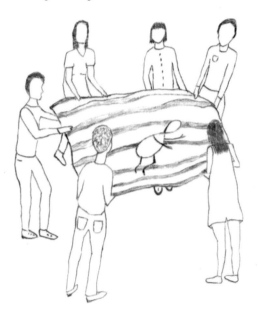

(Fig. 12) This is **The Little You**, who represents you as a child and the feelings that you had when you were very young.

The Little You emerges into the world supported with Unconditional Love. **The Little You** is encouraged to explore, be curious, express creativity and experience adventures. People around **The Little You say:**

"We see you."
"We hear you."
"We love you for where you are in your journey and how you are doing your journey."

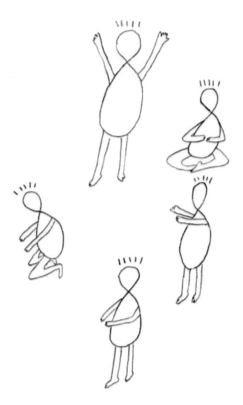

(Fig. 13) Look at the light radiating from the child who is nourished by Unconditional Love.

(Fig. 14) **The Little You** loves to touch family system members. Connection and touch are vital for us to survive childhood. Heart-to-heart connection is cherished above all.

Like many species in the natural world, we need connection in order to survive. So, we connect in whatever way our family system members offer to us. If that is through Unconditional Love, many of our needs are met and we have joyful, happy, secure childhoods.

Conditional Love:
The Little Selves

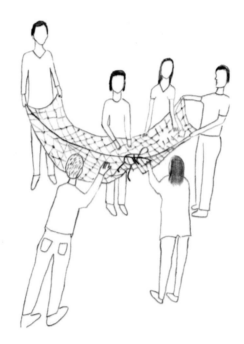

(FIG. 15) **HOWEVER,** parents are human. Grandparents are human. All the family system members are also on their own journeys. They have stresses, difficulties, problems. They make mistakes. At times, they cannot "be present" with Unconditional Love for the child.

While we need and deserve Unconditional Love, the more common experience that children have is that of ... *Conditional Love*. Parents and other family members love the child AND need the child to conform in ways that allow the family members to live their lives with less stress.

When family system members offer Conditional Love, **The Little You** experiences uncertainty. Instead of feeling connected to family members through support, **The Little You's** connections are tenuous, unpredictable, tangled, complicated and desperate.

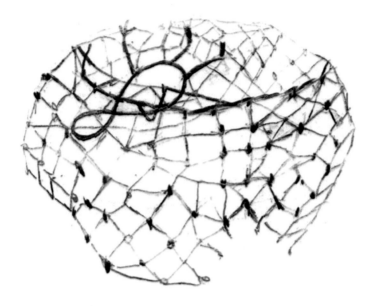

(Fig. 16) What does **The Little You** feel now?

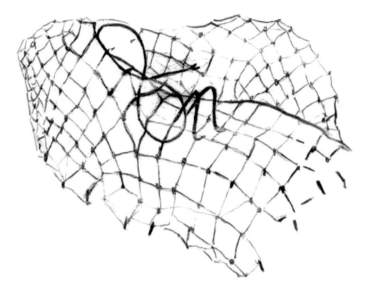

(Fig. 17) And now?

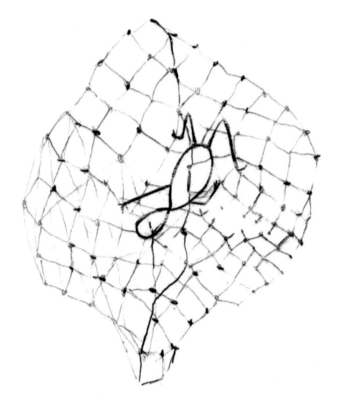

(Fig. 18) And now?

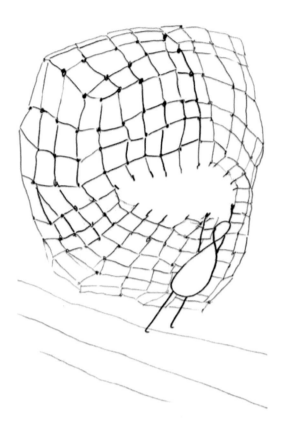

(Fig. 19) And now?

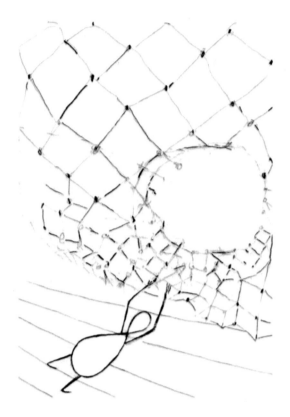

(Fig. 20) And now?

(Fig. 21)

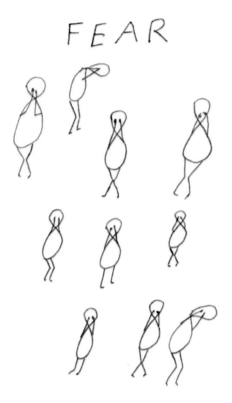

(Fig. 22)

(Fig. 23) Pain, fear, shame.

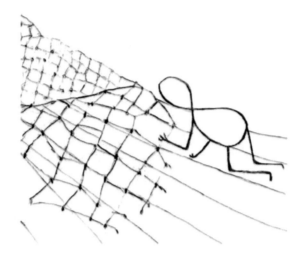

(Fig. 24) **The Little You**, in a desperate attempt to survive the dangers of Conditional Love, frantically scrambles to reconnect to family system members. Otherwise survival is not possible. So what happens?

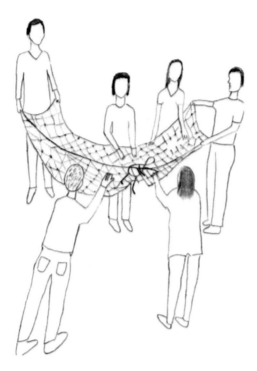

(Fig. 25) **The Little You** grasps the reality: "I have a choice. I can reconnect, or die."

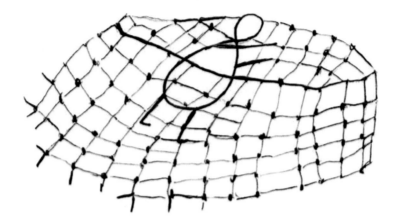

(Fig. 26) Reconnection keeps **The Little You** alive.

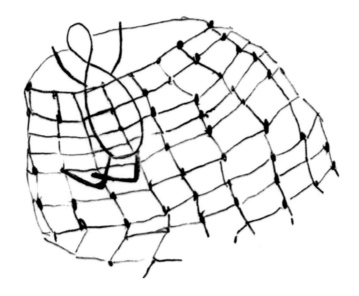

(Fig. 27) Alive, Surviving and Conditionally Loved.

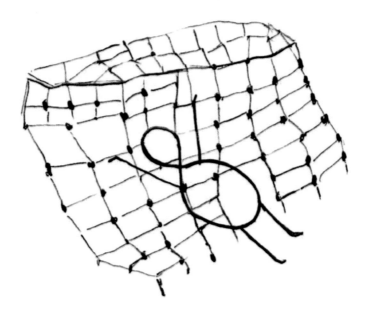

(Fig. 28) Conditional Love … Pain … Fear … Shame.

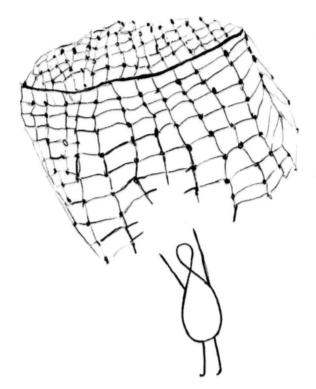

(Fig. 29) Conditional Love ... Pain ... Fear ... Shame.

(Fig. 30) **The Little You** is desperate. "I am tortured by pain, fear and shame. I must survive. I will do whatever I have to do."

To survive, **The Little You** must separate from pain, fear and shame. To do otherwise is not compatible with life.

So, **The Little You** does something brilliant...out of the pain, fear and shame emerges the **Judge**, to separate from the pain, fear and shame. The **Judge** holds and comforts **The Little You**.

(Fig. 31) To survive this situation (which many children would not survive), **The Little You** asks, "Why?" The **Judge**, without hesitation, offers answers.

(Fig. 32) The **Judge's** answers are full of certainty, to counteract the uncertainty of Conditional Love. The certainty convinces and soothes **The Little You** creating *beliefs* which inform *identity*.

The Little You: "Why do I keep falling?" (**Judge:** *Because you are_____(stupid, naïve, clumsy, weak, too trusting, etc...)*

The Little You: "What have I done to deserve this?" (**Judge:** *You are not worthy. You are not lovable. You are too demanding. You are the loser in our family)*

The Little You: "I am a bad kid"

The Little You: "I am stupid"

The Little You: "I am a loser"

What is Judgment?

(FIG. 33) **JUDGMENT** is Separation.

(Fig. 34) The **Judge** separates **The Little You** from pain, fear and shame.

(Fig. 35) The **Judge** is an indiscriminate separator. The **Judge** separates **The Little You** from pain, fear and shame. AND the **Judge** also separates **The Little You** from Essence, the **Connecting-Up Self** who radiates light and who is nurtured by Unconditional Love.

(Fig. 36) The **Judge** is responsible for minimizing all experiences of pain, fear and shame. The **Judge** teaches **The Little You** to *Globalize*...to take a tiny bit of information and *make it true for all time*. When learning the dangers of a hot stove, the parent warns the two-year-old to not touch. The child, driven by curiosity, touches and the hand gets burned. Thus, emerges the **Judge/Globalizer**, who teaches the child to heed future parental warnings.

However, the **Judge/Globalizer** is indiscriminate in its lessons.

The Little You: "Why do I keep falling?" (**Judge:** *Because you are* _____*(stupid, naïve, clumsy,* *weak, too trusting, etc...AND THIS WILL ALWAYS BE SO)*

The Little You: "What have I done to deserve this?" (**Judge:** *You are not worthy. You are not lovable. You are too demanding. You are the loser in our family AND THIS WILL ALWAYS BE SO)*

The Little You: "I am a bad kid" (**Judge:** *YES, YOU ARE. AND THIS WILL ALWAYS BE SO)*

The Little You: "I am stupid" (**Judge:** *YES, YOU ARE. AND THIS WILL ALWAYS BE SO)*

The Little You: "I am a loser" (**Judge:** *YES, YOU ARE. AND THIS WILL ALWAYS BE SO)*

UNLOVABLE

(Fig. 37) **The Judge/Globalizer** promotes the belief "I am Unlovable," insisting, "You are unlovable and have always been unlovable and will always be unlovable."

UNWORTHY

(Fig. 38) **The Judge/Globalizer** promotes the belief "I am Unworthy," insisting, "You are unworthy and have always been unworthy and will always be unworthy."

(Fig. 39) These feelings and thoughts hurt, but they persist. To further separate from the pain, fear and shame, **Judge/ Globalizer** wonders, "What can I do to make the grown-ups happier with me and make me feel more lovable and worthy?"

Over time, the **Judge/Globalizer** learns to behave in certain ways that influence the feelings and behaviors of the grown-ups, creating five additional Little Selves. The **Judge/ Globalizer** and these Little Selves can sometimes make the grown-ups feel happier. This eases the pain, fear and shame for a little while. When they feel happier, **The Little You** feels less unlovable, less unworthy.

(Fig. 40) **Performer/Perfectionist**. From an early age, the Performer/Perfectionist learns to perform well. This makes family system members happy. **The Little You** less unlovable. The Performer/Perfectionist focuses on "getting it right". The Performer/Perfectionist wants to be better than others. The Performer/Perfectionist wants to earn more money. The Performer/Perfectionist wants more accolades.

(Fig. 41) **Intellectual.** From an early age, the Intellectual learns to do well in school and cultivate the Intellect. This makes family system members happy. **The Little You** feels less unlovable. The Intellectual focuses on learning the ABC's, reading, writing, arithmetic, memorizing facts, getting good report cards.

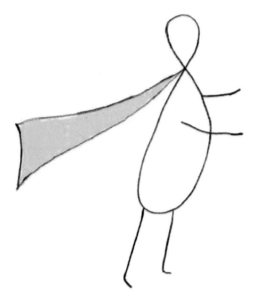

(Fig. 42) **Caretaker**. From an early age, the Caretaker learns to caretake family system members. This makes family system members happy. **The Little You** feels less unlovable. The Caretaker is a fixer. Like a superhero, the Caretaker knows what is best for others.

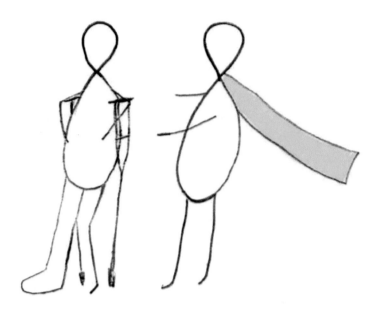

(Fig. 43) Injured Friend is learning to cope with crutches and a cast after sustaining an accident. Caretaker spies an opportunity to help. This assistance is unsolicited by Injured Friend.

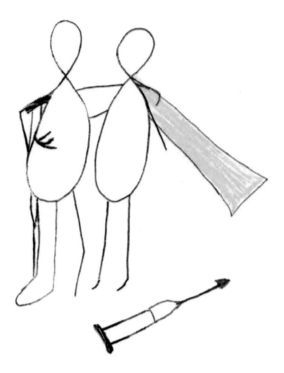

(Fig. 44) Caretaker is very persuasive and convinces Injured Friend to accept care. Injured Friend is tired, in pain, and appreciates the offer of care. Caretaker says, "Let my body replace one crutch." Both benefit from the connection.

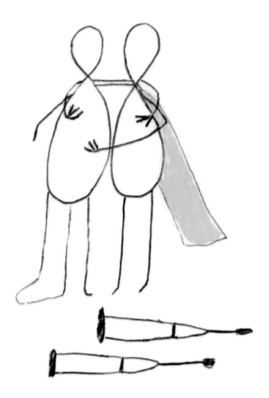

(Fig. 45) Caretaker becomes more involved. "You don't need either crutch. I will hold you." Injured Friend settles into the connection. It is a relief to have someone giving care.

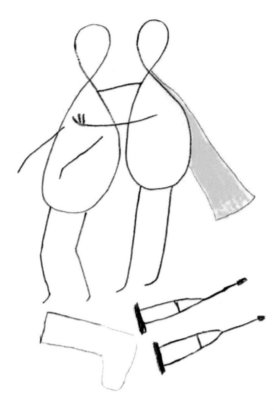

(Fig. 46) Injured Friend's leg heals enough to be free of the cast. The crutches could help with independent mobility. Caretaker persuades, "I can do what the crutches can do, and so much more."

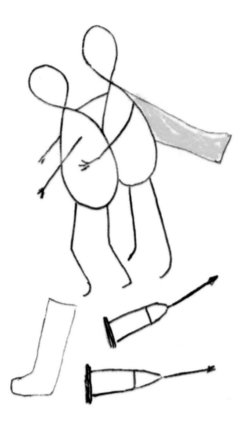

(Fig. 47) Injured Friend is ready for independence. The leg has fully healed. Caretaker expresses doubt. "You are still weak. You could fall and be back where you started. You still need me."

(Fig. 48) Injured Friend relaxes into the persuasive arms of Caretaker. Caretaker's attentions come with a price, with strings attached. Injured Friend must show gratitude, express indebtedness. Caretaker keeps score of what is given and what is received. Caretaker has an insatiable need for positive accolades.

(Fig. 49) The Quartet: **The Judge/Globalizer holding The Little You, joined by Performer/Perfectionist, Intellectual and Caretaker.** These four Little Selves form The Quartet, which helps the **The Little You** survive childhood. It's a successful, brilliant strategy for moving into adulthood and cultivating a career path in many professions.

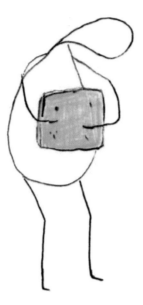

(Fig. 50) **Pain Body**. The actions of *The Quartet*, while effective, are exhausting. At some point, the body gets hurt, sad, tired, depressed, burned out, anxious, panicky, sick. This gives rise to the Pain Body, another Little Self.

The body gives information that can help keep an individual's system in balance. Babies and very young children know what their bodies are saying, and freely express their needs. With age, we lose consciousness of the body's messages.

We can reconnect with the body by learning to listen to it. *The Quartet* makes it hard to listen and creates imbalance. Disease emerges with imbalance.

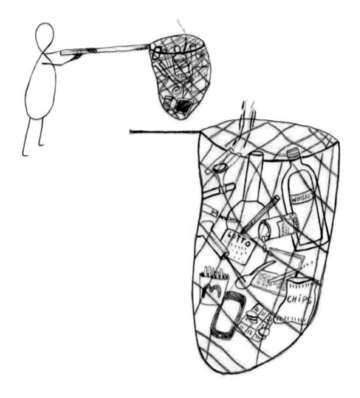

(Fig. 51) **Relief Seeker**. When the Pain Body dominates, after *The Quartet* has created exhaustion, you seek relief. The Relief Seeker looks for relief in anesthesia (drugs, alcohol) and distraction (cigarettes; overworking; gambling; shopping; disordered eating; unconnected sex; screen time with TV, computers, handheld devices).

(Fig. 52) Relief Seeker can be in control for short or long periods of time.

The Parenting of the Little Selves by Your Connecting-Up Self

(FIG. 53) **YOUR Connecting-Up Self**. No child gets out of childhood uninjured. Native Americans refer to the "sacred wounds" from which we all must heal.

The Connecting-Up Self embodies a collection of Parts of Self that parent the Little Selves through Unconditional Love. Your Connecting-Up Self knows *Who You Really Are, Your Essence.* The Connecting-Up approaches life with *emerging consciousness.* The Connecting-Up cherishes relationship, connection and communication, reads, engages in therapy, takes self-help workshops, focuses on listening and calming the mind, learns to eat healthfully, learns to move the body mindfully, connects with nature, and experiences yoga, jin shin jyutsu, acupuncture, meditation, homeopathy, resonance repatterning, and other mind/body/spirit disciplines.

The Connecting-Up develops *Savviness*, an understanding and acceptance of "What Is".

The Connecting-Up develops *Fierceness*, the willingness to stand firmly in your truth and advocate for that truth.

The Connecting-Up learns to parent your Little Selves and helps them develop trust. *The Connecting-Up is the only parent that the Little Selves will ever trust.*

(Fig. 54) As your Connecting-Up Self gets stronger, you become aware of energies that are supporting your journey. You notice *synchronous events*. You understand what it is to be in a state of flow. In *Flow State*, things happen easily.

Your Connecting-Up Self also cultivates your Chosen Family, which is distinct from your family of origin. Chosen Family members are consciously selected by your Connecting-Up Self. They may or may not include some blood family members. *Your Chosen Family is comprised of those who see you, hear you and love you for where you are in your journey and how you are doing your journey.*

(Fig. 55) For **Performer/Perfectionist**, your Connecting-Up Self connects to the Parenting Energy of **Collaborator**.

(Fig. 56) For **Intellectual**, your Connecting-Up Self connects to the Parenting Energy of **Intuitive**.

(Fig. 57) For **Caretaker**, your Connecting-Up Self connects to the Parenting Energy of **Caregiver**.

(Fig. 58) Caretaker's actions differ from Caregiver's actions in motivation and intent. Both engage in Caring. Caretaker, a Little Self, is motivated by feeling unworthy and unlovable, the results of having received Conditional Love. Caretaker's intent is to receive gratitude, accolades and connection. Caretaker says, "I give myself away to be connected."

Caregiver, having received Unconditional Love, recognizes that each person is on a sovereign journey. A caring connection with Caregiver allows both partners to engage with invitation and intention.

(Fig. 59) We can understand Caregiver through rock climbing, which involves tandem climb. Climbers work in pairs. One scales the face of the rock first, hammering steel rods into crevices, and setting ropes until reaching a ledge where there is a place to rest.

(Fig. 60) The second climber then uses the ropes and rods to scale that section of the rock face.

(Fig. 61) While the first climber is resting, the second climber, who had an easier time, goes up the next section of rock face, hammering steel rods and setting the ropes.

(Fig. 62) How can we use this rock-climbing image to understand caring through Caregiver? Imagine standing with another person, facing one another. You, as Caregiver, can state to your partner, "I am on my sovereign journey and you are on yours. Today, we have decided to walk the same path together for a little while. We symbolize this by holding hands. In this way, we join one another. I may be ahead of you during this section of the journey. To symbolize this, I will turn and walk forward, leading you by the hand. I feel joy in sharing with you my ideas and experiences, and having you listen. There is no glory in being in my position and no shame in being in your position."

(Fig. 63) Switch positions. You say to your partner, "Now you are ahead on the journey because I want to learn some things from you. There is no glory in being in your position and no shame in being in my position.

"We both know that we need one another to do this journey in the best possible way for both of us."

(Fig. 64) For **Pain Body**, your Connecting-Up Self connects to the Parenting Energy of **Wise Body**.

When the body becomes ill, there is imbalance in the system. The body's symptoms are giving you messages about imbalance, disharmony. The body knows what it needs. Our challenge is to learn to interpret the messages that the body is giving. The body desires to be in a state of balance, of harmony. This is your *Inner Healer.*

Your body will tell you what it needs, and you can learn to listen, *really listen*, and take action to support the healing process of your body.

(Fig. 65) For **Relief Seeker**, your Connecting-Up Self connects to the Parenting Energy of **Synchronicity Seeker**.

(Fig. 66) Relief Seeker reaches for anesthesia (drugs, alcohol) and distraction (cigarettes; overworking; gambling; shopping; disordered eating; unconnected sex; screen time with TV, computers, handheld devices).

(Fig. 67) Anesthesia and distraction fill a void. Synchronicity Seeker offers something even better to fill that void.

(Fig. 68) Relief Seeker is skeptical, but curious. Relief Seeker is willing to see what Synchronicity Seeker is noticing.

(Fig. 69) Ahhhh ... so beautiful ...

(Fig. 70) Wow ... more and more ...

(Fig. 71) This feels good …

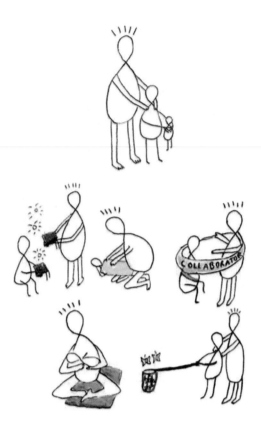

(Fig. 72) For **Judge/Globalizer**, your Connecting-Up Self connects you to the Parenting Energy of *all of this.*

(Fig. 73) The Connecting-Up Self says, "I realize that my experiences with my family of origin gave me some injuries and therefore some challenges. My family of origin did its best with what it knew to do at the time. I understand that 'you can only know what you know when you know it.' This is the essence of being human."

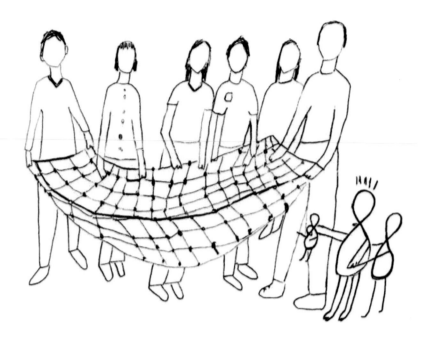

(Fig. 74) "The injuries that I sustained have created imbalances in my life, as evidenced by the challenges I am currently facing."

(Fig. 75) "I am ready to learn what I need to learn to create a more balanced life. I am ready to 'parent' my Little Selves in a way that they will understand."

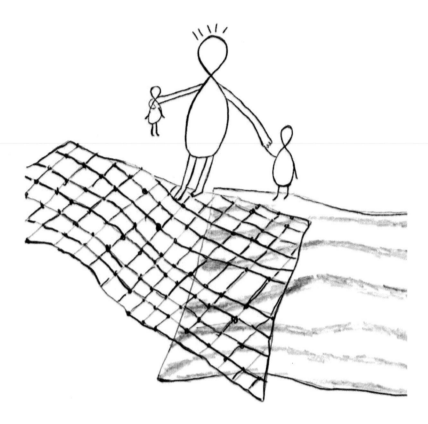

(Fig. 76) "I am aware that my Little Selves will not allow any-one except my Connecting-Up Self to parent them, because they have erected many protective and survival defenses that prevent anyone else from doing that parenting."

(Fig. 77) "My Connecting-Up Self is the only parent that they will trust. I also see that I am ready to cultivate my Chosen Family, which is distinct from my family of origin, and may or may not include some blood family members in it."

(Fig. 78) "My Chosen Family is comprised of those who see who I am, hear what I am saying and love me for where I am in my journey and how I am doing my journey."

The Connecting-Up message is: "I can only know what I know when I know it."

- *Parents to children:* "What I knew at the time that you were a child did not fulfill all of your needs. I hurt you. I did not intend to. *I did my best with what I knew at the time.*"

- *Connecting-Up to Little Selves:* "What the grown-ups knew when we were little did not fulfill all of our needs. We got hurt. They did not intend to hurt us. *They did their best with what they knew at the time.* Now it is time for me to help you take care of all of the needs that we have."

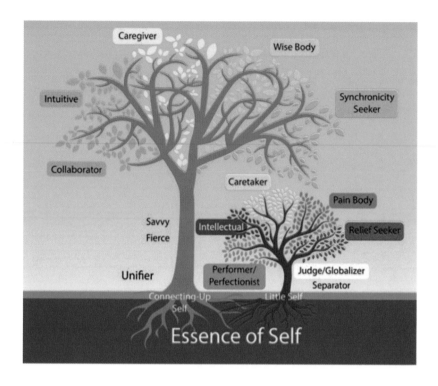

(Fig. 79) The Connecting-Up Self Tree is next to the Little Self Tree in the forest. It grows taller and taller during the energy-moving awareness and consciousness work in which you are engaging.

Like a tree that becomes part of the canopy of the rainforest, the Connecting-Up Self Tree eventually shades the Little Self Tree, protecting it, and also keeping it from getting much sunlight and rainfall, so that it doesn't grow as strong as the Connecting-Up Self Tree.

For Performer/Perfectionist, the Connecting-Up Self connects to the Parenting Energy of Collaborator.

For Intellectual, the Connecting-Up Self connects to the Parenting Energy of Intuitive.

For Caretaker, the Connecting-Up Self connects to the Parenting Energy of Caregiver.

For Pain Body, the Connecting-Up Self connects to the Parenting Energy of Wise Body.

For Relief Seeker, the Connecting-Up Self connects to the Parenting Energy of Synchronicity Seeker.

For Judge/Globalizer, the Connecting-Up Self connects to the Parenting Energy of *all of this*.

The Connecting-Up Self says:

"I realize that my experiences with my family of origin gave me some injuries and therefore some challenges. My family of origin did its best with what it knew at the time. I understand that 'you can only know what you know when you know it.' This is the essence of being human.

"The injuries that I sustained have created imbalances in my life, as evidenced by the challenges I am currently facing. I am ready to learn what I need to learn to create a more balanced life. I am ready to 'parent' my Little Selves in a way that they will understand. I am aware that my Little Selves will not allow anyone except my Connecting-Up Self to parent them, because they have erected many protective and survival defenses that prevent anyone else from doing that parenting. My Connecting-Up Self is the only parent that they will trust.

"I also see that I am ready to cultivate my Chosen Family, which is distinct from my family of origin, and may or may not include some blood family members in it. My Chosen Family is comprised of those who see who I am, hear what I am saying and love me for where I am in my journey and how I am doing my journey."

Invitation: Create an Odyssey Chosen Family Circle

YOU ARE INVITED to create a Chosen Family Circle and continue to explore the work that you have begun. An ideal Circle size is between five and nine individuals. You may meet in person or via cyberspace. An Odyssey Facilitator will meet virtually with your Circle.

Each Circle meeting lasts two hours, and the first phase involves eighteen meetings, twice a month for nine months. Once you have assembled your Circle, choose someone to connect with an Odyssey Facilitator via the Odyssey website, www.odysseyjourney.com. Write an email through the "Contact Us" link on the website, and you will receive further guidance.

Your Publishing Opportunity: The Odyssey Family Systems Project

STORY IS ONE of our most powerful ways of connecting with one another and healing. The Odyssey Family Systems Project offers the opportunity for you to share your stories with others who will benefit from their healing power.

You may participate in the Project as an individual, or in collaboration with members of your Odyssey Chosen Family Circle. Connect with your Odyssey Facilitator (www.odyssey-journey.com) to discuss options and opportunities.

About the Author

Kathryn Hayward, MD lives in Mallorca, Spain, and is a leader in the field of Integrative Health in the United States and Europe. In 2012, she retired from her position as Associate Physician at the Massachusetts General Hospital (MGH) and Assistant Professor of Medicine at Harvard Medical School. She practiced primary care internal medicine at MGH from 1992 until 2009, and then consulted with the Benson Henry Institute for Mind Body Medicine until 2010. In 2004, she created a private Integrative Health practice, Odyssey Journey: A Collaborative Approach to Wellness (www.OdysseyJourney. com), which brings together what she regards as the four disciplines that comprise Integrative Health: conventional medicine, movement, whole, plant-based food and mind/body/ spirit disciplines. From 2007-2012, she served as one of the two Harvard representatives to the Consortium of Academic Health Centers for Integrative Medicine (CAHCIM) and, from 2011-2013, served that group as core faculty, and in 2013, as Program Director of the LEAPS into IM program for medical students. In 2014 and 2015, she joined the core faculty of HEART-IM, a program for fourth year medical students affiliated at the time with the University of Wisconsin. She was the founder of the Collaborative Medicine Working Group later renamed the Integrative Health Collaborative in Boston, and is a co-founder of International Integrators, a global community dedicated to the promotion of Integrative Health (www.internationalintegrators.org). **International Integrators** publishes articles on Integrative Health topics in its blog, supports Integrative Health projects worldwide and offers Living Whole immersion retreats.

About the Artist

Maia Evarista Charlotte Ibar is a French-Basque and American artist who works across mediums including painting, video, installation and performance. She received her MFA in painting from The New York Studio School in 2009, and attended Pratt Institute, Parsons Paris and recently The Mountain School of Arts, MSA in Los Angeles. In 2014, Maia co-founded the gallery and artist residency Pioche Projects in Biarritz, France, where she curates artists and projects from a variety of creative, healing, scientific and spiritual practices. Her musical/visual and performance projects go under the names *Dual-Split, Rita and The Labyrinth, Four Winds Bath*, and *Lighter*. She has been working with an ongoing passion for the power of frequencies, tones, colors, taste, smells and sounds to use therapeutically. Maia has been giving sound bath journeys since 2011 and is now giving private sound healing sessions. Maia has been investigating her artistic processes as rituals connected and related to the mind, body and spirit. The journey and process are a way to teach herself and others about the subconscious, revealing for her the deepest emotions and the path that her life has given her. With Kathryn Hayward and other colleagues, Maia is also a co-founder of **International Integrators**.

About the Digital Consultant

Jack Temple, MD is an Internal Medicine physician in Southern California. At the time he worked on this book, he was a third-year medical student at Rush University. After graduation, he did an internship, residency, and chief residency in Internal Medicine at the University of California-San Diego. He was first introduced to *Odyssey Family Systems* in the summer of 2012 when he attended the Leadership & Education Program for Students in Integrative Medicine (LEAPS). He was immediately struck by the simple yet incredibly complex dynamics held within these teachings. He worked closely with Kathryn Hayward and many other collaborators to graphically depict the core concepts of *Odyssey Family Systems*. He is constantly amazed at how universal these principles are and how often they present themselves in his life at home and in the clinic. Jack is also a co-founder of **International Integrators**.

About the creation of the graphic description of the Odyssey paradigm

Jack Temple collaborated with Kathryn Hayward and Kristy King, who at the time was a medical student and now is a physician, to bring into graphic form the "Two Trees" image of the Odyssey paradigm that depicts the Little Selves and the corresponding parenting energies of the Connecting-Up Self. For several years, Kathryn had been developing the image of the two trees. When she described it to Jack and Kristy, their creative imaginations and graphic artistry ignited. The final image was graphically created by Jack. This was one of the many joy-filled, "synchronous" adventures associated with the Odyssey Family Systems workshops and the creation of this Guide.

Made in the
USA
Columbia, SC